Theory of Music Grade 3
May 2018

COL

Your full name (as on appointment form). Please use BLOCK CAPITALS.

_____

Your signature

_____

Registration number

_____

Centre

_____

Instructions to Candidates

1. The time allowed for answering this paper is **two (2) hours.**
2. Fill in your name and the registration number printed on your appointment form in the appropriate spaces on this paper, and on any other sheets that you use.
3. **Do not open this paper until you are told to do so.**
4. This paper contains **seven (7) sections** and you should answer all of them.
5. Read each question carefully before answering it. Your answers must be written legibly in the spaces provided.
6. You are reminded that you are bound by the regulations for written exams displayed at the exam centre and listed on page 4 of the current edition of the written exams syllabus. In particular, you are reminded that you are not allowed to bring books, music or papers into the exam room. Bags must be left at the back of the room under the supervision of the invigilator.
7. If you leave the exam room you will not be allowed to return.

Examiner's use only:

1 (10)	
2 (15)	
3 (10)	
4 (15)	
5 (15)	
6 (15)	
7 (20)	
Total	

(A-03)

Section 1 (10 marks)

Put a tick (✓) in the box next to the correct answer.

Example

Name this note:

A ☐   D ☐   C ☑

This shows that you think **C** is the correct answer.

1.1   Name the circled note:

E ☐   G ☐   A ☐   ☐

1.2   Add the total number of quaver beats in these tied notes:

9 ☐   8 ☐   7 ☐   ☐

1.3   Which time signature is in compound time?

6/8 ☐   **3/4** ☐   ¢ ☐   ☐

1.4   Which is the correct time signature?

4/4 ☐   **3/4** ☐   **6/8** ☐   ☐

1.5   The major key with two sharps in its key signature is:

G major ☐
D major ☐
B♭ major ☐   ☐

Boxes for examiner's use only

Put a tick (✓) in the box next to the correct answer.

1.6   What does *tranquillo* mean?

Sweetly ☐
Lightly ☐
Calmly ☐

1.7   Which note is the tonic of the major key shown by this key signature?

G ☐   F ☐   B♭ ☐

1.8   Name this interval:

major 7th ☐
minor 7th ☐
major 6th ☐

1.9   Name this triad:

tonic triad of F major in root position ☐
tonic triad of F major in second inversion ☐
tonic triad of D minor in second inversion ☐

1.10   Which chord symbol fits above this dominant triad?

A ☐   C ☐   Em ☐

Please turn over for Section 2

Section 2 (15 marks)

2.1   Write a one-octave B melodic minor scale in crotchets, going up then down. Do not use a key
       signature, but write in any necessary accidentals.

2.2   Write the key signature of the key shown. Then write its one-octave arpeggio in the rhythm
       given below.

       D major, going down then up

Section 3 (10 marks)

3.1   Circle five different mistakes in the following music, then write it out correctly.

Boxes for
examiner's
use only

Section 4 (15 marks)

4.1   Transpose this tune down an octave into the bass clef to make it suitable for a cello to play.

Armstrong-Gibbs

Section 5 (15 marks)

5.1   Using minims, write out balanced 4-part chords for SATB using the chords shown by the Roman numerals. Double the root in each case and make sure that each chord is in root position.

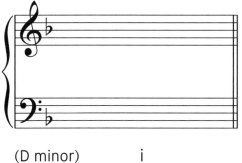

(D minor)   i

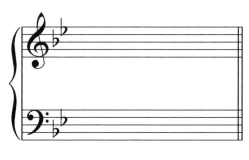

(B flat major)   I

Section 6 (15 marks)

6.1   Use the root of each triad shown by the chord symbols to write a bass line.

Please turn over for Section 7

Section 7 (20 marks)

Look at the following piece and answer the questions opposite.

Haydn (adapted)

Boxes for
examiner's
use only

7.1   In which key is this piece? _____

7.2   Which note is the dominant in this piece?_____

7.3   What do you notice about the treble and bass parts in bars 1-3?

        _____

7.4   What does **Allegretto** mean? _____

7.5   Write a chord symbol above the chord in bar 8 to show that the dominant triad should
        accompany it.

7.6   From which bar should the music repeat after bar 16?_____

7.7   What is the interval between the two notes marked with asterisks (*) in bars 4 and 5?

        _____

7.8   What type of beat is shown in the time signature? _____

7.9   Write appropriate Roman numerals below the final crotchet beat in bar 15 and the first crotchet
        beat in bar 16.

7.10   What cadence is formed by these two chords? _____

Theory of Music Grade 3
May 2018

COLLEGE LONDON

Your full name (as on appointment form). Please use BLOCK CAPITALS.

_____

Your signature

Registration number

_____   _____

Centre

_____

Instructions to Candidates

1. The time allowed for answering this paper is **two (2) hours**.
2. Fill in your name and the registration number printed on your appointment form in the appropriate spaces on this paper, and on any other sheets that you use.
3. **Do not open this paper until you are told to do so.**
4. This paper contains **seven (7) sections** and you should answer all of them.
5. Read each question carefully before answering it. Your answers must be written legibly in the spaces provided.
6. You are reminded that you are bound by the regulations for written exams displayed at the exam centre and listed on page 4 of the current edition of the written exams syllabus. In particular, you are reminded that you are not allowed to bring books, music or papers into the exam room. Bags must be left at the back of the room under the supervision of the invigilator.
7. If you leave the exam room you will not be allowed to return.

(B-03)

Section 1 (10 marks)

Put a tick (✓) in the box next to the correct answer.

Example

Name this note:

A ☐   D ☐   C ☑

This shows that you think **C** is the correct answer.

1.1   Name the circled note:

A# ☐   F# ☐   C# ☐   ☐

1.2   Add the total number of quaver beats in these tied notes:

4 ☐   5 ☐   6 ☐   ☐

1.3   Which is the correct time signature?

9 ☐   **3** ☐   **2** ☐   ☐
8   **4**   **2**

1.4   Which time signature is in compound time?

3 ☐   **6** ☐   **3** ☐   ☐
8   **8**   **2**

1.5   The relative minor of D major is:

D minor ☐
E minor ☐   ☐
B minor ☐

1.6   What is the tonic of the minor key shown by this key signature?

E ☐   D ☐   A ☐   ☐

2

Put a tick (✓) in the box next to the correct answer.

1.7   Here is the scale of D harmonic minor. Which degree(s) of the scale will you change to make the scale of D melodic minor?

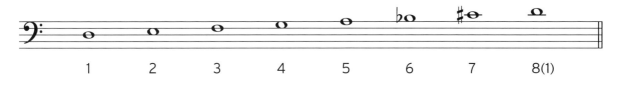

7th degree ☐   6th degree ☐   6th & 7th degrees ☐

1.8   Which chord symbol fits above this dominant triad?

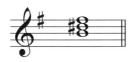

B ☐   Bm ☐   D ☐

1.9   Name this interval:

major 6th ☐   major 7th ☐   minor 7th ☐

1.10   Name this triad:

tonic triad of A minor in second inversion ☐
tonic triad of A minor in first inversion ☐
tonic triad of C major in root position ☐

Please turn over for Section 2

Section 2 (15 marks)

2.1   Write a one-octave B melodic minor scale in minims, going up then down. Use the correct
      key signature and add any necessary accidentals.

2.2   Using quavers, write a broken chord of B♭ major tonic triad (going up). Use patterns of four
      notes each time. Finish on the first B♭ above the stave.

Section 3 (10 marks)

3.1   Circle five different mistakes in the following music, then write it out correctly.

Section 4 (15 marks)

4.1   Transpose this tune down an octave into the bass clef to make it suitable for a bassoon to play.

French trad.

Section 5 (15 marks)

5.1   Using minims, write out 4-part chords for SATB using the chords shown by the Roman numerals. Double the root in each case and make sure that each chord is in root position.

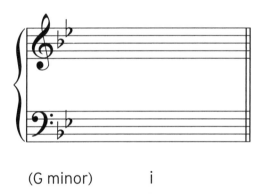

(G minor)   i

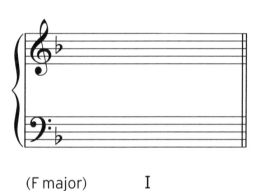

(F major)   I

Section 6 (15 marks)

6.1   Use the root of each triad shown by the chord symbols to write a bass line.

Please turn over for Section 7

Section 7 (20 marks)

Look at the following piece and answer the questions opposite.

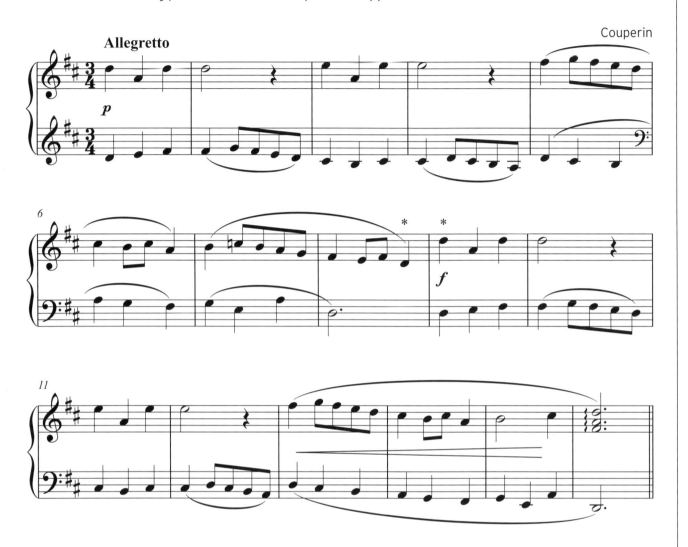

7.1   In which key is this piece? _____

7.2   Which note is the leading note in this piece? _____

7.3   Compare bars 1-4 with bars 9-12. What two differences do you notice? _____

        _____

        _____

7.4   Write a chord symbol above the first crotchet in bar 3 to show that the dominant chord
        accompanies the tune here.

7.5   Does this piece start on an up-beat or a down-beat? _____

7.6   Look at bar 3. Do the treble and bass parts move in similar or contrary motion?

        _____

7.7   What is the interval between the two notes marked with asterisks (*) in bars 8 and 9?

        _____

7.8   What type of beat is shown in the time signature? _____

7.9   Write a Roman numeral below the final note in this piece to show that the tonic chord
        accompanies the music here.

7.10   What does **Allegretto** mean? _____

THEORY OF MUSIC PAST PAPERS – MAY 2018 GRADE 3

for Trinity College London written exams

This booklet contains two past exam papers for Trinity College London's Grade 3 exam in music theory, taken from the May 2018 exam sessions. There is no difference in difficulty between the A and B papers.

This booklet can be used in conjunction with the corresponding model answers, which are available to download from **trinitycollege.com/pastpapers**, where you will also find past papers and model answers from other exam sessions.

Download model answers and additional past papers from **trinitycollege.com/pastpapers**

The Theory of Music Workbook series contains all the requirements of the graded exams and provides step-by-step instructions, suitable for use in lessons or for private study.

Theory of Music Workbook Grade 3	TG 006523	ISBN 978-0-85736-002-1
Theory of Music Workbook Grade 4	TG 006530	ISBN 978-0-85736-003-8

Also available from **trinitycollege.com/shop** or your local music shop:

Handbook of Musical Knowledge	TCL 001191	ISBN 978-0-85736-015-1
A6 Manuscript Jotter	TG 009418	ISBN 978-0-85736-189-9

All syllabuses and further information about Trinity College London exams can be obtained from **trinitycollege.com**

TCL 018816
ISBN 978-0-85736-796-9

9 780857 367969